Kitten
MATH

the world's most adorable math project

FOR KIDS AGES 8-12

by Kelli Pearson

ISBN: 978-0-9855725-3-2

Cover art by Tjarda Borsboom

Brain Spark Publishing
P.O. Box 2924
Santa Clara, CA 95055

https://artfulmath.com

for Jimmy

TABLE OF CONTENTS

"Mew! Mew! Mew!"

Imagine...you hold in your hands a soft, squirmy kitten baby, feeding her with a bottle the size of your thumb. **You are dying. How could anyone resist such cuteness??**

Meanwhile, three more kittens are squealing at the top of their baby lungs, climbing your leg with tiny needle claws and scrambling for their turn at the bottle. **They are yours to care for, and they are adorable.**

Welcome to the world of fostering! You have just taken in four, 3-week-old kittens who have no mama. It's your job to keep them healthy, safe, and loved until they are old enough to be adopted.

Along with bottle feeding your kittens every few hours, you'll weigh them on a scale, go shopping for toys and supplies, design a kitten room, and so much more!

Your kittens may be imaginary, but everything you will learn about fostering and caring for orphan kittens is real. **By the time you finish Kitten Math, you'll be better at math and an expert at fostering kittens!**

Take Kitten Math to the next level with...

- Adorable videos of tiny foster kittens
- Printable game boards and demo game videos
- Interview with 11-yr-old Avery, who fosters kittens
- Coloring pages, kitten drawing, and more!

**Get your FREE kitten bonuses at
artfulmath.com/kitten-goodies**

There is MATH in this book!

I know, with a name like "Kitten Math" that probably isn't much of a surprise, but I thought I should warn you anyway.

If you're usually NOT a math person, you'll be happy to know that math is a lot more fun with kittens. I mean, isn't EVERYTHING more fun with kittens??

Stuff you should know...

You are not SUPPOSED to be good at all the math in this book.

Not knowing and then finding out is called "learning".

Learning is the point.

You can go SLOW and still be good at math.

Take your time. Look closely. Think and figure things out. This is way more important than spitting out math facts like a robot.

NO FAIR giving up and saying you're bad at math.

You get better by trying. You try and make mistakes. Try and make mistakes. And little by little, you

What to do if you don't know how to do the math...

- Tell yourself, "**I don't know this yet... but I'm still learning**"

- **Take your time** and see if you can figure it out on your own

- **Ask someone** to explain it to you

- **Look at the answer key**, then see if you can get that answer

- If you're still unsure, **skip it and come back later**

The most important thing is to have fun. Kittens are the BEST way to learn math!

KITTENS COME HOME

Picking Out Your Kittens

The "I Love My Kittens" Game

Kitten Name Math Code

DAY 1: PICKING OUT YOUR KITTENS

You're in the middle of breakfast when your mom gets a text...

MOM: Oh wow, someone just dropped off a litter of kittens at the animal shelter, and they're asking if we can foster them. Should we take some kittens?

YOU: YAAAYYYYYEEEESSSSSSSSS!!!!!!!

MOM: Ok then... (texts the shelter). Let's go get some kittens!

You walk into the shelter, and there are kittens EVERYWHERE.

The shelter worker tells you it's "kitten season"—the time of the year when the weather is warmer, and thousands of kittens are being born...

SHELTER WORKER: Whew, it's crazy around here! People are bringing in kittens EVERY DAY, and the little ones need sooo much care. Thank goodness for fosters like you!

YOU: Is fostering like adopting a kitten?

SHELTER WORKER: A little bit. Fosters have kittens for just a little while. They take care of kittens who are too little or too sick to be adopted yet. Then they go to their forever homes.

YOU: So I'm like these kittens' mama right now?

SHELTER WORKER: Yup, exactly! You'll have to do all the things their mama would normally do: give them food, keep them warm, keep them clean, help them go potty...

Oh look! They're bringing out your kittens now!

A volunteer comes bustling out with a **cardboard box full of kittens**.

"Here you go!" she says. "Go ahead and pick out the ones you want to bring home."

"Just four?" you ask. "Just four!" says mom.

Which kittens will you bring home?

Write their numbers: _____ _____ _____ _____

Your kittens are exactly 3 weeks old. **When was their birthday?** _____

They can be adopted at 8 weeks old. **What date is that?** _____

Each of your kittens is so unique and beautiful!! **What will you name them? Draw and describe your foster kittens in the boxes below.**

NAME: _____

_____
_____
_____
_____

NAME: _____

_____
_____
_____
_____

NAME: _____

_____
_____
_____
_____

NAME: _____

_____
_____
_____
_____

THE "I LOVE MY KITTENS" GAME

1. **Roll a die** to fill in the spaces below.
2. **Add the numbers** to find the answer to each kitten question.

How many times can you kiss your kittens in one minute?

___ + ___ + ___ + ___ = [ ]

How many kitten photos can you take in one hour?

___ + ___ + ___ + ___ + ___ = [ ]

How many times will you snuggle with your kittens each day?

___ ___ + ___ = [ ]

How many times each day will your kittens do something CRAZY?

___ ___ + ___ ___ = [ ]

Write your own question:

_____

___ ___ + ___ ___ + ___ ___ = [ ]

DAY 2: KITTEN NAME MATH CODE

Let's play a game with your kittens' names! Here is a number code.
Each letter is worth money: A = $1, B = $2, and so on.

A	B	C	D	E	F	G	H	I	J	K	L	M
$1	2	3	4	5	6	7	8	9	10	11	12	13

N	O	P	Q	R	S	T	U	V	W	X	Y	Z
14	15	16	17	18	19	20	21	22	23	24	25	26

1. How much is each kitten's name worth? Add the letters to find out!

    - Kitten 1 name _____ $_____

    - Kitten 2 name _____ $_____

    - Kitten 3 name _____ $_____

    - Kitten 4 name _____ $_____

2. How much are all 4 kitten names added together? $_____

3. How much is YOUR first name worth? $_____

4. How much is your full name worth? $_____

5. What's a kitten name that is close to $100? _____

6. What is the most expensive word you can think of?

    _____ $_____

DAY 3: PLAY "CROSS OUT SINGLES" GAME

*Print the "Cross Out Singles" game boards and watch the video of how to play this game at **artfulmath.com/kitten-goodies**.*

PLAYERS: 2-8 players

YOU NEED: a game board for each player, and one die

PART 1: ROLL FOR NUMBERS

1. **Give a game board to each player**.

2. **Roll the die.**

3. **All the players write that same number** in any one of their empty boxes.

4. **Roll nine times**, so that all the boxes are filled in.

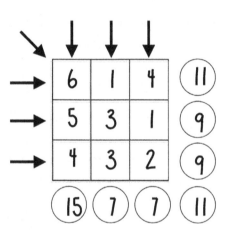

PART 2: ADD YOUR NUMBERS

5. **Add the numbers and write the sum in the circles.**
   - Add the rows **across**
   - Add the columns **down**
   - Add **diagonally** from left to right

PART 3: FIND YOUR SCORE

6. Look at the numbers in the circles. **Cross out any number that does NOT have a match** in another circle.

7. **Add the circle numbers that are NOT crossed out. This is your score.**

   (In the example above, Kitty Cat crossed out 15. Her score was 54.)

KITTEN SHOPPING

What Do Baby Kittens Need?

Poopy Puzzles

Do You Have Enough Money?

Going Kitten Shopping

Think of Decimals Like Money

DAY 4: WHAT DO BABY KITTENS NEED?

Match the kitten info to its photo and number to complete the sentence.

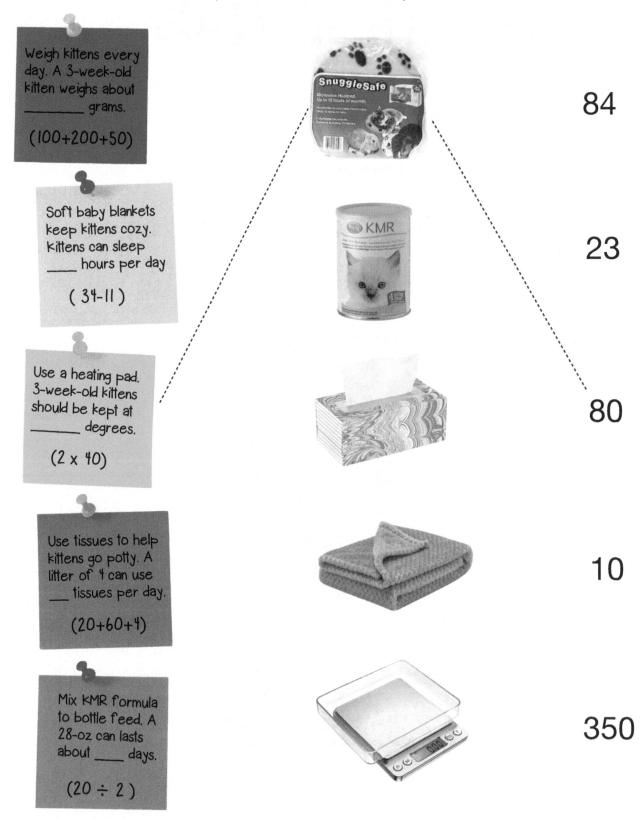

Weigh kittens every day. A 3-week-old kitten weighs about _____ grams.

(100+200+50)

Soft baby blankets keep kittens cozy. Kittens can sleep ____ hours per day

(34-11)

Use a heating pad. 3-week-old kittens should be kept at _____ degrees.

(2 x 40)

Use tissues to help kittens go potty. A litter of 4 can use ___ tissues per day.

(20+60+4)

Mix KMR formula to bottle feed. A 28-oz can lasts about ____ days.

(20 ÷ 2)

84

23

80

10

350

POOPY PUZZLES

Solve the puzzles below to get a sense of **how many swaddle blankets, wipes, and tissues you'll need** to buy when you go kitten shopping.

1. A swaddle blanket is made of thin, soft fabric and can be used to clean, feed, or comfort kittens. Your first week with fosters, you used a LOT of swaddle blankets:

- 10 swaddle blankets got **pooped on or peed on**
- you used 8 to **dry off kittens** after giving them butt baths
- two were used to **wrap kittens up** so they would feel snug and safe
- 5 got all **milky from bottle feeding**
- three were used to **clean up messes** in the kitten playpen

How many swaddle blankets did you wash in one week? _____

If you had just 4 swaddle blankets, how many loads of laundry would you have to do that week? _____

If you had 7 swaddle blankets, how many loads of laundry would you have to do that week? _____

2. Tiny kittens can't go to the bathroom by themselves—you have to help them go potty by rubbing their bottoms with a tissue. There are three levels of messy:

PEE (level 1): 3 tissues and 1 wet wipe

SMALL POOP (level 2): 3 tissues and 2 wet wipes

BIG MESSY POOP (level 3): 3 tissues, 4 wet wipes, and 1 towel for butt bath

In one day, your kitten Tinkle peed 6 times, had one small poop, and one big, messy poop. You used _____ tissues, _____ wipes, and _____ towels.

If all 4 of your kittens had peed and pooped exactly like Tinkle that day, you would have used _____ tissues, _____ wipes, and _____ towels.

DAY 5: DO YOU HAVE ENOUGH MONEY?

A budget is like an allowance with a certain amount of money to spend.

It's almost time to go shopping for your kittens.

You will have a budget of $250 to spend at the pet store!

You'll need to keep track of how much money you've spent, so you know how much more stuff you can buy. Here's a shortcut that may help you:

"Rounding" means using a nearby number that's easier to remember.

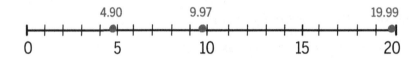

The price $4.90 is close to $5.00. We can **round up** to $5.00 to make adding easier.
Rounding is helpful when we don't need the exact amount; we just need to get close.

$9.97 rounds to _____ $19.97 rounds to _____

You can also **round down** to an easy number. $15.03 rounds to _____

Round the prices to the nearest dollar:

$14.99 >>_____ $9.50 >> _____

$25.15 >>_____ $8.99 >>_____

$13.47 >>_____ $7.30 >>_____

$5.95 >>_____ $7.90 >>_____

Why do you think so many prices in stores end in .99?

_____

DAY 6: GOING KITTEN SHOPPING

Look at the Pet Store catalog on the next 2 pages. Choose supplies for your kittens.

You have a budget of $250. Try to spend as much of the $250 as you can.

Write the names and prices of each item in the chart below.

ITEM	PRICE
GRAND TOTAL	

Formula and bottles, please!

Don't forget the kitty beds!

KITTEN LOVE ♥ PET STORE
BABY KITTY CATALOG

Soft Cave Cat Bed

Extra thick furry cat bed is machine washable. Makes cats feel safe and cozy.

$ 23.32

Plush Round Cat Bed

Deliciously soft, snuggly round kitten bed. Size small.

$ 20.98

Kitten Cave

Eco-friendly kitten bed for hiding, sleep, and play. Easy to clean.

$ 14.99

Cat and Kitten Bed

High, fluffy sides makes cats feel safe and secure. Machine washable.

$ 16.43

Heating Pad

Snuggle Safe stays hot for up to 10 hours. Just heat up in the microwave.

$ 25.99

Zoo Animals Blanket

Plush baby blanket with super soft fleece and fluffy sherpa backing.

$ 12.99

Cozy Kittens Blanket

Fuzzy, soft pink baby blanket has an adorable kitten print.

$ 7.20

Cuddly Bears Blanket

Cozy, warm mink blanket with sherpa backing. Black and white bear print.

$ 9.90

Soft Minky Blanket

Super soft, plush blanket with dotted grey backing and sweet grey bears.

$ 9.90

Ultra Soft Blanket

Fleece, plush blankets for babies. Snuggly and lightweight.

$ 18.99

Swaddle Blankets

Soft, thin mini-blankets are the perfect size for feeding time. 100% cotton. 7 count.

$ 9.99

Soft Swaddle Blankets

Four sweet receiving blankets for feeding or swaddling kittens.

$ 7.99

Burt's Bees Shampoo

Gentle, all-natural baby shampoo is unscented and safe for kittens.

$ 8.99

Snuggle Kitty

"Real feel" heartbeat eases crying & loneliness. Mimics the feel of mama cat.

$ 39.95

Calming Cat Toy

Press the pillow to activate the electronic purring sound.

$ 1.49

Peek & Play Pop Up Toy

Super fun kitty play mat has crinkle floor, hanging toys, and peep holes.

$ 10.62

Pet Nursing Bottles

Two 2-oz bottles with nipples.

$ 3.99

Nursing Kit

One 2-oz bottle with nipples and bottle cleaner.

$ 2.99

Miracle Nipple

The only nipple that kittens can't bite off and swallow. Fits bottles & syringes.

$ 14.49

Kitten Play Mat

Fun first toy for kittens. Includes dangling jingle balls, fuzzy ball, & mouse.

$ 13.59

Pet Playpen

A safe, secure living space for kittens 2-6 weeks old. Fits a litter of 6 kittens.

$ 28.97

Cardboard Cat Carrier

Disposable carrier is easy to assemble and great for one-time use.

$ 2.50

Cat Carrier

Soft-sided, comfortable cat carrier with shoulder strap and pockets.

$ 19.90

Weighmax Scale

Removable bowl. Weighs in grams or ounces. Size 7.2 inches across.

$ 13.78

Flushable Wet Wipes

Gentle cleaning. Safe for kittens and environment. Biodegradable. 252 count.

$ 9.84

Unscented Wipes

No fragrances or dyes. Safe and gentle for kittens. 480 count.

$ 12.49

Kleenex Tissues small

Small pack of ultra-soft tissues. 4 boxes, 65 tissues per box.

$ 5.97

Kleenex Tissues large

Large pack of ultra-soft tissues. 8 boxes, 120 tissues per box.

$ 12.35

DAY 7: THINK OF DECIMALS LIKE MONEY

We write "six dollars and seventeen cents" with a decimal (dot) like this: **$6.17**

Money is written as decimals. When you understand money, you can understand decimals. **Think of decimal number places as dollars, dimes, and pennies.**

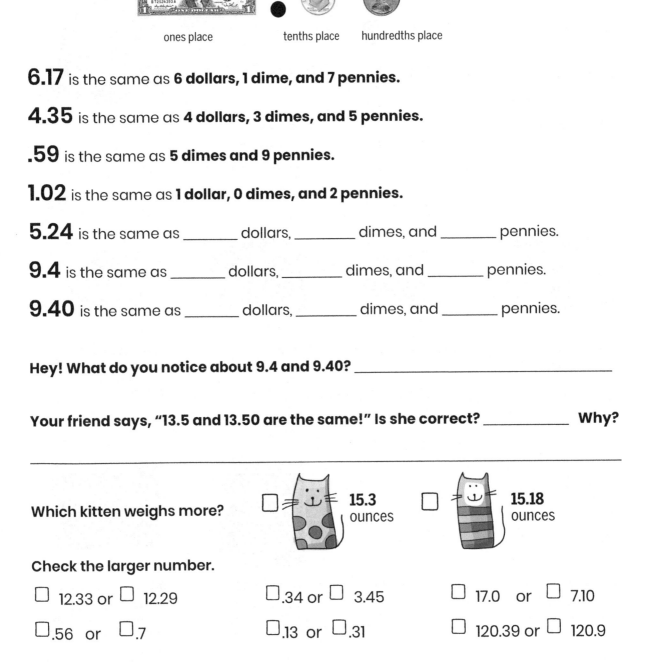

ones place   tenths place   hundredths place

6.17 is the same as **6 dollars, 1 dime, and 7 pennies.**

4.35 is the same as **4 dollars, 3 dimes, and 5 pennies.**

.59 is the same as **5 dimes and 9 pennies.**

1.02 is the same as **1 dollar, 0 dimes, and 2 pennies.**

5.24 is the same as _____ dollars, _____ dimes, and _____ pennies.

9.4 is the same as _____ dollars, _____ dimes, and _____ pennies.

9.40 is the same as _____ dollars, _____ dimes, and _____ pennies.

Hey! What do you notice about 9.4 and 9.40? _____

Your friend says, "13.5 and 13.50 are the same!" Is she correct? _____ **Why?**

_____

Which kitten weighs more? ☐ **15.3** ounces   ☐ **15.18** ounces

Check the larger number.

☐ 12.33 or ☐ 12.29   ☐ .34 or ☐ 3.45   ☐ 17.0 or ☐ 7.10

☐ .56 or ☐ .7   ☐ .13 or ☐ .31   ☐ 120.39 or ☐ 120.9

These two number lines are connected. The first one is like counting dimes. The second one is like counting pennies. **What are the small lines between 0.5 and 0.6?**

_____

_____

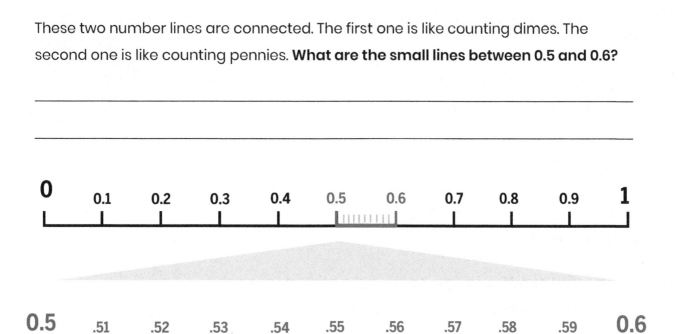

Answer the questions below. If you get stuck, the number lines will help you.

 Fluffpug gained .57 ounces today.

 Sasquatch gained .9 ounces today.

Who gained more weight? _____

Did Sasquatch gain more or less than half an ounce? _____

Did Fluffpug gain more or less than one ounce? _____

Fluffpug's brother Floppy gained MORE than 0.5 ounces, but LESS than 1 ounce.
How much weight might Floppy have gained? _____ ounces

Sasquatch's sister Spunky Monkey gained MORE than 0.9 ounces, but LESS than 1 ounce. **How much weight might Spunky have gained?** _____ ounces

DAY 8: PLAY "ROUND FOUR" GAME

Print the "Round Four" game boards and watch the video
*of how to play this game at **artfulmath.com/kitten-goodies**.*

PLAYERS: 2 players

YOU NEED: 2 dice, markers in 2 colors, one Round Four game board

PART 1: GET READY

1	2	3	4	5	6	7
11	12	13	14	15	16	17
21	22	23	24	25	26	27
31	32	33	34	35	36	37
41	42	43	44	45	46	47
51	52	53	54	55	56	57
61	62	63	64	65	66	67

1. Use the Round Four game board in the back of the book, or print one from artfulmath.com/kittens-goodies

2. Each player chooses their own colored marker.

PART 2: PLAY

3. Roll three dice.

4. **Make a decimal number** with the digits. With a 5, 6, and 1 you could make...

   65.1   5.61   .165   15.6   5.61   and so on

5. **Round the decimal** to the nearest whole number.

   .651 rounds to 1   65.1 rounds to 65   15.6 rounds to 16

1	2	3	4	5	6	7
11	12	13	14	15	16	17
21	22	23	24	25	26	27
31	32	33	34	35	36	37
41	42	43	44	45	46	47
51	52	53	54	55	56	57
61	62	63	64	65	66	67

6. **Circle that number** on the game board.

7. **Take turns rolling** and circling numbers on the board.

8. The first person to get **four in a row** in their color wins.

FEEDING SCHEDULE

How Often Should Kittens Eat?

Set Up A Feeding Schedule

Kitten Feeding Puzzlers

Spending Time With Kittens

DAY 9: HOW OFTEN SHOULD KITTENS EAT?

**"Mom, these kittens are hungry AGAIN.
How often do kittens need to eat, anyway?"**

Mom's not sure, so you ask Annabel, the shelter worker. Here's her reply:

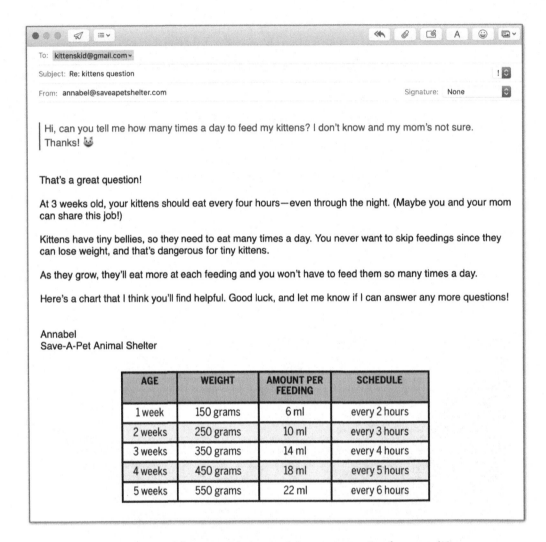

To: kittenskid@gmail.com

Subject: Re: kittens question

From: annabel@saveapetshelter.com   Signature: None

> Hi, can you tell me how many times a day to feed my kittens? I don't know and my mom's not sure. Thanks! 😺

That's a great question!

At 3 weeks old, your kittens should eat every four hours—even through the night. (Maybe you and your mom can share this job!)

Kittens have tiny bellies, so they need to eat many times a day. You never want to skip feedings since they can lose weight, and that's dangerous for tiny kittens.

As they grow, they'll eat more at each feeding and you won't have to feed them so many times a day.

Here's a chart that I think you'll find helpful. Good luck, and let me know if I can answer any more questions!

Annabel
Save-A-Pet Animal Shelter

AGE	WEIGHT	AMOUNT PER FEEDING	SCHEDULE
1 week	150 grams	6 ml	every 2 hours
2 weeks	250 grams	10 ml	every 3 hours
3 weeks	350 grams	14 ml	every 4 hours
4 weeks	450 grams	18 ml	every 5 hours
5 weeks	550 grams	22 ml	every 6 hours

What's the most important thing you learned from Annabel's email?

_____

What's one question you still have?

_____

Let's take a closer look at the chart Annabel sent you.

AGE	KITTENS' WEIGHT	AMOUNT PER FEEDING	HOW OFTEN
1 week	150 grams	6 ml	every 2 hours
2 weeks	250 grams	10 ml	every 3 hours
3 weeks	350 grams	14 ml	every 4 hours
4 weeks	450 grams	18 ml	every 5 hours
5 weeks	550 grams	22 ml	every 6 hours

How often should you feed your 3-week-old kittens? _____

How much should a 3-week-old kitten eat **per feeding**? _____

How many times per day should you feed a 3-week-old kitten? _____
(Hint: there are 24 hours in a day.)

What does "ml" mean? ▢ millipedes ▢ millionaires ▢ milkshakes ▢ milliliters

You are fostering a 3-week-old kitten. Your friend is fostering a 4-week-old kitten.
Which kitten needs to be fed **MORE TIMES** per day? _____

How much should a 3-week-old kitten eat **per day**? _____ ml

Look at the **KITTENS' WEIGHT** column. What pattern do you see?

_____

Look at the **AMOUNT PER FEEDING** column. What pattern do you see?

_____

DAY 10: MAKE A FEEDING SCHEDULE

A feeding schedule is a daily calendar that tells you what time to feed your kittens each day. **As they grow, they'll eat less often but eat more at each feeding.**

Answer the questions, then fill in the feeding schedules below:

1. What time do you wake up in the morning? _____

2. **Write this as the FIRST time** on the feeding schedule in the chart below. Then figure out all the other feeding times from there.

3. Who will feed your kittens when you're at school or sleeping? _____

4. **Add their name** to the feeding schedule at the times when you aren't available.

FEEDING SCHEDULE FOR 3-WEEK-OLD KITTENS

3-week-old kittens eat every 4 hours. Our tummies are very tiny!

TIME	WHO WILL FEED

Three-week-old kittens eat every 4 hours. How many times a day is that?

A 3-week old kitten eats _____ times a day.

FEEDING SCHEDULE FOR 4-WEEK-OLD KITTENS

4-week-old kittens eat about every 5 hours (more or less).

TIME	WHO WILL FEED

Four-week-old kittens eat **every 5 hours**. There are **24 hours** in a day.

What might be tricky about your feeding schedule? _____

24 hours					= one day
5 hours	5 hours	5 hours	5 hours	5 hours	= 25 hours

FEEDING SCHEDULE FOR 5-WEEK-OLD KITTENS

5-week-old kittens eat every 6 hours.

TIME	WHO WILL FEED

How many times a day will you feed 5-week-old kittens? _____ times per day

DAY 11: KITTEN FEEDING PUZZLERS

A one-week-old kitten eats every 2 hours.

If Fluffernutter eats at 5:00pm, she'll need to eat again

at _____ and _____

A two-week-old kitten eats every 3 hours.

If Sammy eats at 12:00 noon, he'll need to eat

again at _____ and _____

A three-week-old kitten eats every 4 hours.

If Millie eats at 9:00am, she'll need to eat

again at _____ and _____

A four-week-old kitten eats every 5 hours.

If Jellybean eats at 3:00 pm, he'll need to eat

again at _____ and _____

SPENDING TIME WITH KITTENS

It's been a busy day, but now you have one hour of free time before bed. **How many minutes is that?** _____

You want to divide your time equally between TWO kitten activities.

ONE HOUR

What two kitten activities will you do in that hour?

_____ and _____

How much time will you spend on each activity?

_____ minutes

The next day, you decide to do FOUR fun kitten activities in your hour of free time.

ONE HOUR

What four kitten activities will you do in that hour?

_____   _____

_____   _____

How much time will you spend on each activity?

_____ minutes

On Saturday, you can't get enough of your adorable kittens, so you peek in on them every 5 minutes! **How many times do you peek at your kittens in 1 hour?** _____

On Sunday, you play with your kittens every 8 hours. **How many times a day do you play with your kittens?** _____ times a day

Each one of your Sunday play times was 10 minutes long. **How many minutes did you play with your kittens in one day?** _____ minutes

DAY 12: PLAY "SPEEDY SCHOOL DAY" GAME

*Print the "Speedy School Day" game boards and watch the video of how to play this game at **artfulmath.com/kitten-goodies**.*

PLAYERS: 2-4 players
YOU NEED: Speedy School Day game board, one die, round clock (optional)

*Here's a game that will give you **magic powers to speed up your school day** so you can get home to your kittens faster!*

1. Start at 9:00, the beginning of your school day. **Roll the die.**

2. **Multiply that number times 10.**

3. **Speed forward that many minutes in your day.**

    You rolled a 6. Speed forward 60 minutes.
   6 x 10 = 60

4. **Write the new time on your paper.**
   If you added 60 minutes to 9:00, write 10:00 on your paper.

5. **Take turns rolling** and moving ahead in your school day until one player reaches 3:00.

6. All the other players get one more turn.

7. If you make it home to your kittens, you are a winner!

BOTTLE FEEDING KITTENS

How To Bottle Feed A Kitten

Mixing Kitten Formula

Kitten Ratio Puzzlers

Are Your Kittens Eating Enough?

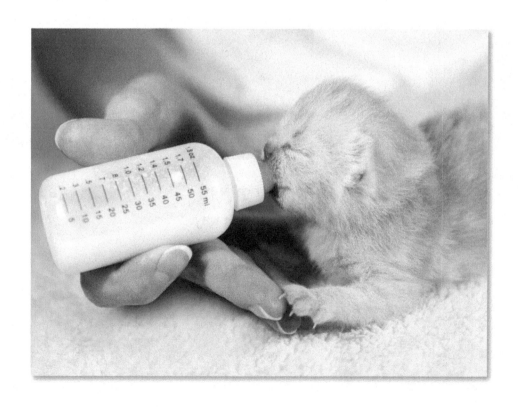

DAY 13: HOW TO BOTTLE FEED A KITTEN

It's feeding time, and thank goodness you discover a couple more notes inside the kitty carrier that Annabel, the shelter worker, sent home with you:

Never feed a kitten on its back—it's dangerous! Feed belly-down, like nursing mama cat.

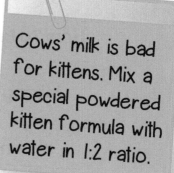

Cows' milk is bad for kittens. Mix a special powdered kitten formula with water in 1:2 ratio.

Which of these are the right way to feed a kitten?

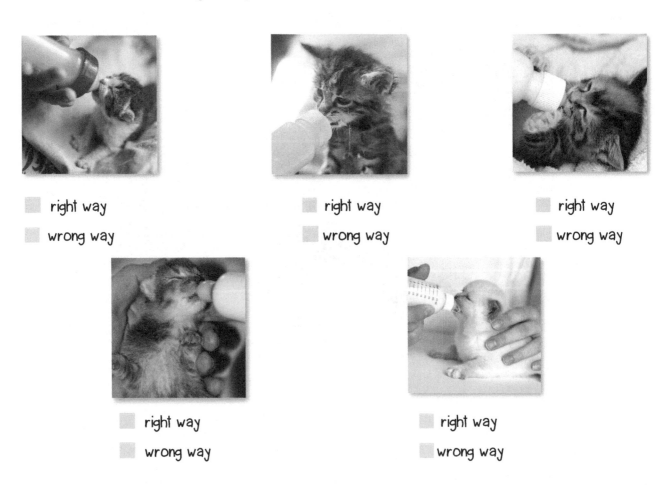

□ right way
□ wrong way

□ right way
□ wrong way

□ right way
□ wrong way

□ right way
□ wrong way

□ right way
□ wrong way

MIXING KITTEN FORMULA

One of the sticky notes says to mix kitten formula in a **1 : 2 ratio**.
You scratch your head. What does that even mean?

A ratio is a pattern, a special relationship between numbers.
Can you spot the pattern for mixing kitten formula?

The ratio is 1:2 . For every ONE scoop of powder, add 2 scoops water.

1 scoop powder   2 scoops water

2 scoops powder   4 scoops water

3 scoops powder   6 scoops water

How much **WATER** would you mix with 1 scoop of powder? _____

How much **WATER** would you mix with 6 scoops of powder? _____

How much **POWDER** would you mix with 4 scoops of water? _____

How much **POWDER** would you mix with 8 scoops of water? _____

KITTEN RATIO PUZZLERS

1. Your friend Samantha is fostering older kittens who are eating wet food. She gives TWO spoonfuls of food to each kitten.

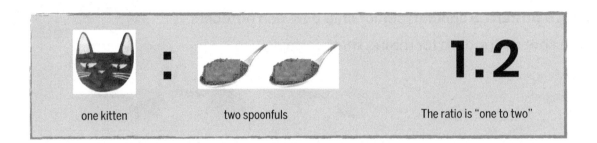

one kitten : two spoonfuls   The ratio is "one to two"   1:2

When every ONE kitten gets TWO spoonfuls, we say the ratio is "one to two".

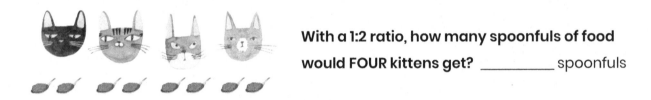

With a 1:2 ratio, how many spoonfuls of food would FOUR kittens get? _____ spoonfuls

With a 1:2 ratio, how many spoonfuls would SIX kittens get? _____ spoonfuls

2. A week later, Samantha's kittens are bigger, and they are eating more. She now gives THREE spoonfuls of wet food to each kitten.

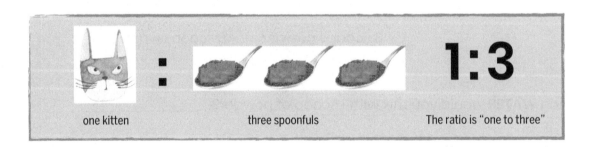

one kitten : three spoonfuls   The ratio is "one to three"   1:3

With a 1:3 ratio, how many spoonfuls would FOUR kittens get? _____ spoonfuls

With a 1:3 ratio, how many spoonfuls would FIVE kittens get? _____ spoonfuls

DAY 14: ARE YOUR KITTENS EATING ENOUGH?

Mew! Mew! Mew! You have four hungry kittens squealing and wanting a turn at the bottle.

You give the bottle to one kitten, and then another, and then another...

But wait! How much did that first kitten eat? Is your littlest kitten eating enough? Are some kittens eating more than others?

One way to find out is by looking at the bottle to see how much they ate.
(Another is by weighing kittens. We'll do that in the next chapter.)

Before we explore if our kittens are eating enough, let's examine a kitten bottle:

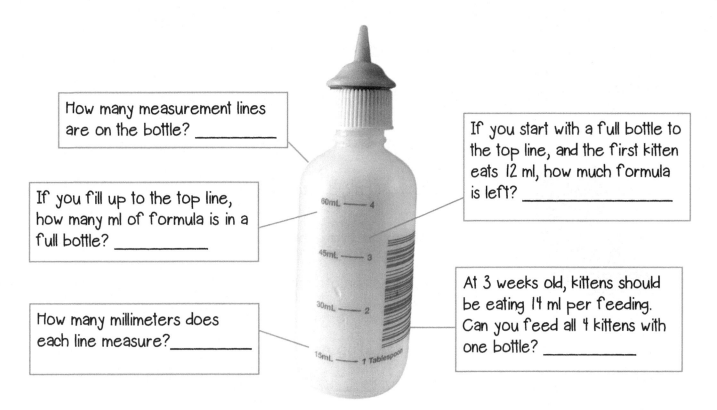

How many measurement lines are on the bottle? _____

If you fill up to the top line, how many ml of formula is in a full bottle? _____

How many millimeters does each line measure?_____

If you start with a full bottle to the top line, and the first kitten eats 12 ml, how much formula is left? _____

At 3 weeks old, kittens should be eating 14 ml per feeding. Can you feed all 4 kittens with one bottle? _____

A	B	C	D	E
You fill a bottle and give it to Kitten #1.	Kitten #1 finishes eating. Kitten #2 starts drinking from the bottle.	Kitten #2 finishes eating. Kitten #3 starts drinking from the bottle.	Kitten #3 finishes eating. Kitten #4 starts drinking from the bottle.	Kitten #4 finishes eating.

A 3-week-old kitten should eat around 14 ml per feeding.

How much did Kitten #1 eat? _____ ml

How much did Kitten #2 eat? _____ ml

How much did Kitten #3 eat? _____ ml

How much did Kitten #4 eat? _____ ml

Which kitten ate the least? _____

Which kitten ate the most? _____

Your kittens should eat about 14ml per feeding. Are they eating enough? ☐ yes ☐ no

Explain:

_____

DAY 15: PLAY "EUCLID'S GAME"

*Print a "Hundred Chart" and watch the video of how to play this game at **artfulmath.com/kitten-goodies**.*

PLAYERS: 2 players

YOU NEED: "Hundred Chart" to use as the game board

PART 1: GET READY

1. The first player picks any number 1–100 and circles it.

2. The second player circles a different number that is NOT double or half of the first number.

PART 2: PLAY

3. Choose any two circled numbers.

4. Subtract the smaller number from the bigger one.

5. Circle the difference (the answer to the subtraction problem).

6. Take turns. Each player picks any two circled numbers, subtracts the smaller one, and circles the difference.

7. The last player to circle a number wins the game.

WEIGHING KITTENS

Weighing Your Kittens

Becoming a Kitten Detective

DAY 16: WEIGHING YOUR KITTENS

You learned from Annabel that it's important to weigh your kittens and write down their weights every day.

When a kitten loses weight, that's a danger sign that your kitten may be sick.

Write your kittens' names in the spaces below.

Often, weight is your only clue that something is wrong—and you might need to get that kitten to the vet, fast! A healthy kitten should gain at least 10 grams per day.

Write the names of <u>your</u> kittens in the spaces below.
Use their weights as clues to answer the questions.

WEIGHT CHART (in grams)

KITTEN NAMES	4-1	4-2	4-3	4-4	4-5	4-6	4-7
	355	380	385	382	369	397	411
	360	379	394	403	420	436	451
	342	362	381	394	405	415	439
	358	375	396	372	373	390	412

Which kitten **gained the most weight** in one week? _____

How much weight did it gain? _____ grams

Which kitten **gained the least weight?** _____ How much? _____ grams

What is the most weight that any kitten **gained in one day**? _____ grams

What is the most weight that any kitten **lost in one day**? _____ grams

BECOME A KITTEN DETECTIVE

Today you will make a line graph for one of your kittens.
Which kitten will you make a line graph for? _____

Look at the weight chart on Day 15 for that kitten. **Write dots** on the line graph below to show that kitten's weights. Then **connect the dots**.

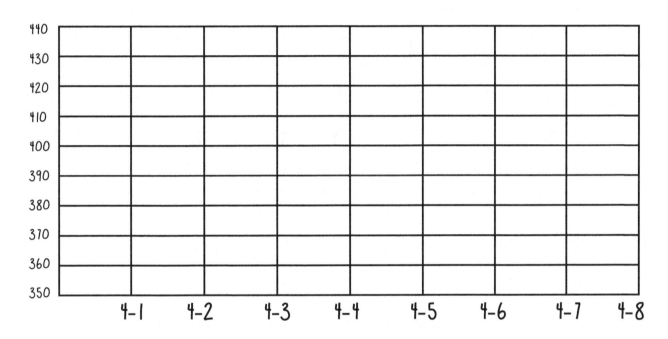

Losing weight is a "red flag" that tells you something is wrong. **Did this kitten lose weight at any point during this week?**   yes   no

What do the weights reveal about your kitten's health during these 7 days?
     Healthy   Got sick, but then got better   Sick all week long

What would a line graph of a sick kitten NOT look like? Circle one.

How can you tell by looking at a kitten's weights when they start feeling better?

_____

This **line graph** that shows the weights of one of your kittens for one week.

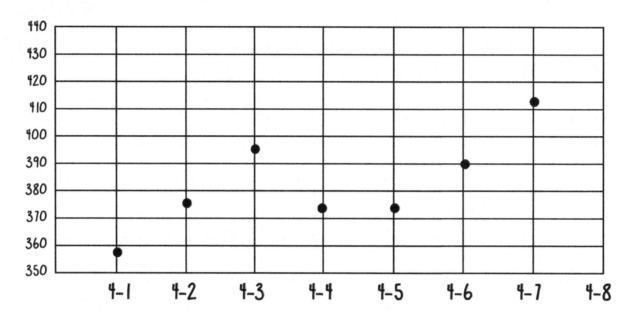

Connect the dots from right to left to complete the line graph.

Which kitten's data is shown on this graph? *(HINT: Match the numbers with the chart on the previous page.)* _____

There are numbers along the **side of the graph:** 350, 360, 370 and so on.

What do these numbers mean?   ▫ weight in grams   ▫ dates   ▫ number of kittens

There are numbers along the **bottom of the graph:** 4-1, 4-2, 4-3 and so on.

What do these numbers mean?   ▫ weight in grams   ▫ dates   ▫ number of kittens

What do the **round dots** show? _____

If your kitten stays healthy, **what do you predict your kitten's weight might be on 4-8?** _____ grams

Draw a dot at that weight on 4-8. Connect the dots.

DAY 17: PLAY "SNUGGLENUMBER" GAME

*Print the "Snugglenumber" game boards and watch the video of how to play this game at **artfulmath.com/kitten-goodies**.*

PLAYERS: 2 or more players

YOU NEED: Snugglenumber game board for each player, one die

PART 1: GET READY

1. The game board shows numbers with lines next to them. You will fill in the lines with numbers 0-9 as you play.

2. Your goal is to make a number on the lines that is as close as possible to the number it's next to.

0 ___

5 ___

10 ___ 3

25 2 6

50 ___ ___

100 6 ___

PART 2: PLAY

3. Roll the die. All of the players write that number in a space on their board. Once a number is written, it can't be erased or moved.

4. Take turns rolling the die and filling in more spaces on your board.

5. There is a trash can at the bottom of the game board. One of the numbers rolled goes in the trash can. (Again, once it's written you can't change it.)

6. Play until all the spaces are filled, then take turns reading your answers out loud. Who got closest to each number?

KITTENS GROW UP

DAY 18: WHAT DO GROWING KITTENS NEED?

Your kitties are growing fast and learning new skills. It's time to buy new supplies.
Draw a line to match kitten skills with the photo and the supplies you'll need to buy.

KITTEN SKILLS	PHOTO	SUPPLIES
cuddle and wrestle		scratching post
eat from a dish		litter box
go potty in litter box		stuffed animal toys
scratch, sharpen claws		kitten food & dishes
jump		balls, toy mice
flying bird toys		flying bird toys

45

HALF OFF ALL KITTEN TOYS

Good news... All kitten toys will be 50% off tomorrow!

→ **50% = "fifty percent".** How would you read these numbers?

        20%   35%   90%   100%

→ **The word "percent" means "out of 100".**

- **A hundred percent** on a test is 100/100...an A+ perfect score!
- **Ten percent** is a low battery—just 10/100. (Where's that charger?)   10% 🔋
- **Fifty percent** is 50/100, or half (since 50 is half of 100).

PERCENTS ARE LIKE FRACTIONS

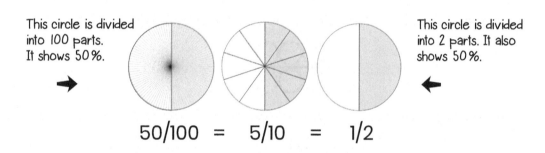

This circle is divided into 100 parts. It shows 50%.

This circle is divided into 2 parts. It also shows 50%.

$$50/100 \ = \ 5/10 \ = \ 1/2$$

Find the 50% off sales price for these kitten toys:

50% off of $6.00 is ___$3.00___   50% off of $12.04 is _____

50% off of $24.00 is _____   50% off of $30.18 is _____

50% off of $8.00 is _____   50% off of $28.60 is _____

50% off of $14.20 is _____   50% off of $10.12 is _____

50% off of $42.88 is _____   50% off of $16.30 is _____

DAY 19: HALF OFF TRICKY NUMBERS

What if you need to divide an odd number in half? Here are two ways to do it.

1. THE DRAWING TRICK

1. To find half of 3, draw three circles in a row.
2. Draw a line down the middle.
3. How many circles on each side of the line?

Half of 3 is 1 $\frac{1}{2}$

2. THE "ADD ONE" TRICK

1. **Start with an odd number.**

   Half of 5 is ???

2. **Add one to make an even number. Then divide *that* number in half.**

   Half of 6 is 3

3. **Subtract 1/2 to get your answer**. (You're giving back the extra one you borrowed.)

   Half of 5 is 2 1/2

FIND HALF OF AN ODD NUMBER WITH MONEY

If a price ends an odd number of cents like .99, add one penny then divide it in half.

50% off $9.99 is ___$5.00_____   50% off $11.99 is _____

50% off $5.99 is _____   50% off $15.99 is _____

50% off $4.27 is _____   50% off $8.15 is _____

50% off $16.49 is _____   50% off $26.13 is _____

50% off $12.99 is _____   50% off $23.99 is _____

50% off $6.99 is _____   50% off $22.99 is _____

DAY 20: SHOPPING FOR BIG KITTENS

Look through the **Big Kitten Catalog** on the next page to buy supplies for your growing kittens. **You have a budget of $200 to spend. All toys are 50% off today!** Take half off the price listed in the catalog (toys only—everything else is regular price).

ITEM	PRICE
GRAND TOTAL	

Lots of toys, please!

Wet food, dry food, and maybe a doggie chew toy!

KITTEN LOVE ♥ PET STORE
BIG KITTY CATALOG

Cat Dancer Chasers

Pack of 6 fun toys with bright fleece. Lightweight for kittens to carry.

$ 3.64

Cat Tracks Ball Toy

Fun puzzle toy for chasing, hunting, and playing with the spinning balls.

$ 8.99

Tunnel and Toys

24 of kitty's favorite toys, plus a fun, pop-up kitty tunnel.

$ 10.50

Feather Teaser Wand

Flying feathers look like birds. Great for jumping, hunting, and playing.

$ 10.95

Toy Variety Pack

Includes feather wand, bell balls, mice, springs, and more.

$ 12.95

Crinkle Balls

Lightweight colorful balls have an irresistible crinkly sound that cats love.

$ 6.99

Foam Soccer Balls

Tiny, adorable soccer balls are lightweight, colorful, and fun.

$ 2.99

Fur Toy Mice

These realistic mice have a rattling sound that makes kittens crazy.

$ 5.04

Platypus Kicker Toy

Huggable, kickable, chewable platypus.

$ 8.99

Kitty Toy Springs

Who knew such a simple toy could be so much fun?

$ 1.79

Mad Cat Taco Toy

Plush toy with knotted strings for kicking, carrying, and chasing.

$ 4.99

Kong Octopus Toy

Fuzzy soft fur and crinkle sound for playing, kicking, and cuddling.

$ 9.21

2-Way Scratcher Toy

Mini scratching post and slide scratcher with spring ball.

$ 15.80

Scratch Post Hammock

Elevated cat hammock on two, 19-inch scratching posts.

$ 25.99

Floor Scratcher

Recycled cardboard scratcher is just the right size for growing kittens.

$ 7.25

Tall Scratching Post

Sisal-wrapped scratching post and hanging cat toy. 32 inches tall.

$ 21.09

Saucer-Style Cat Dish

Shallow ceramic cat food dish has a sweet kitty design. Good for kittens.

$ 6.46

Small Cat Dish

Blue, shallow dish is the perfect size for young kittens. Durable plastic.

$ 2.99

Two Cat Food Dishes

Cute, saucer-style ceramic dishes are the perfect size for kittens. Green and pink.

$ 7.98

Babycat Dry Food

For kittens age 3 weeks and up. Special formula for young kittens.

$ 19.79

Babycat Wet Food

Moist, tasty, soft food made for young kittens.

$ 16.64

Kitten-Safe Litter

Recycled paper pellets are eco-friendly and safe for kittens. 26 pound bag.

$ 18.99

Feline Pine Cat Litter

100% fresh pine pellets. Fresh scent. Safe for kittens. Two 20-lb bags.

$ 27.50

Small Litter Box

Easy to clean, odor and stain resistant.

$ 2.99

Disposable Litter Box

Will not leak, tear, or shred. 100% biodegradable paper. Lasts 4 weeks. 3-pack.

$ 5.93

Litter Box Starter Kit

Comes with medium-size litter box, litter mat, and scoop.

$ 14.50

Cat Litter Scoop

Sturdy metal scoop with soft handle.

$ 9.99

Litter Genie

Special trash can for litter keeps your kitten room smelling fresh and clean.

$ 17.99

DAY 21: PLAY "THE HALF GAME"

*Watch the video of how to play this game at **artfulmath.com/kitten-goodies***

PLAYERS: 2 or more players

YOU NEED: deck of cards

PART 1: GET READY

1. Take out the tens, jacks, queens and kings from the deck.

2. Put the deck face down in the middle of the table.

3. Aces = 1

PART 2: PLAY

4. Take a card from the deck. Don't show the other players.

5. The other players also take a card from the deck without showing anybody.

6. What is half your number? Say your half number out loud. The other players say their half numbers.

> 5 — "My half number is two and a half."
>
> 8 — "My half number is four."

7. The player with the highest number takes the other players' cards.

8. Play more rounds until all the cards are gone. The person with the most cards at the end of the game wins.

DESIGN A KITTEN ROOM

DAY 22: WHAT IS AREA?

Before you set up your kitten room, you'll need to know how much floor space you have to work with. **We measure floor space with area.**

Both of these rectangles are the same length (8 feet long) but the second rectangle has a bigger **a_ _ _** .

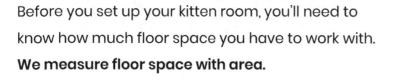

8 feet

8 feet

Area is the amount of space inside a shape. Let's say that once more, because it's important: **Area is the amount of _____ inside a _____.**

We measure area by filling the space with squares. Then we count the squares. In the rectangles below, each square stands for one foot. How many squares are in each of these rectangles? **Count the squares to find the area.**

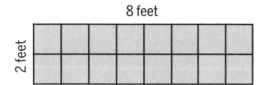

8 feet

2 feet

The area of this rectangle is

_____ square feet

8 x 2 = _____ square feet

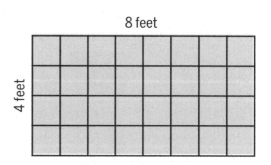

8 feet

4 feet

The area of this rectangle is

_____ square feet

8 x 4 = _____ square feet

The picture below shows a map of a kitten room. A map of a room is called a **blueprint**.

Each of the squares [ ] represents 1 foot across and 1 foot down. This is called **one square foot.**

How many square feet are in this kitten room? There are two ways to find out.

1. **Count the squares.** The number of squares is the area in square feet. (Remember to count the squares UNDER the furniture as well.)

I counted _____ squares. The area is _____ square feet.

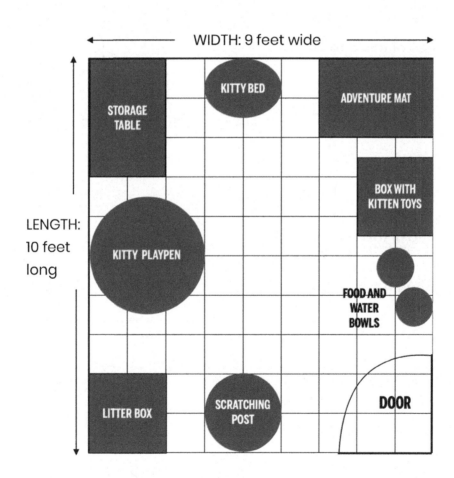

2. A shortcut is to **multiply length times width.** Length = 10 feet, width = 9 feet.

10 x 9 = _____ The area is _____ square feet

KITTEN ROOM AREA PUZZLES

What is the area of each of these kitten rooms?

1. What is the area of this kitten room?

_____ square feet

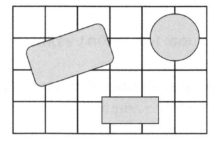

2. What is the area of this kitten room?

_____ square feet

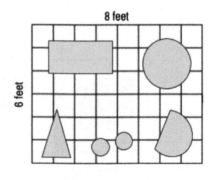

3. What is the area of this kitten room?

_____ square feet

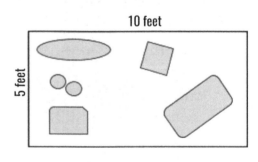

4. What is the area of this kitten room?

_____ square feet

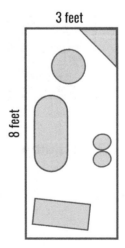

DAY 23: WHAT GOES IN THE KITTEN ROOM?

What will you put in your kitten room (aside from kittens)?
Answer the questions below, then follow the instructions
at the bottom of the page to make your supply list.

Where will you sit? _____

Where will the kittens sleep? _____

How many litter boxes?_____   How many food dishes?_____

Where will you store toys and small supplies? _____

Where will you store blankets and extra beds? _____

Will you have a scratching post? _____

Any other large toys like a tunnel or play mat? _____

Is there any other furniture or floor lamps in your kitten room? _____

MAKE YOUR LIST OF KITTEN ROOM SUPPLIES

1. **Turn to Day 25.** You will see a chart at the top of the page.

2. **Write in the chart a list of things you want in your kitten room.**

3. Don't worry about the length and width right now. You will fill that in later.

HOW TO DRAW OBJECTS ON A MAP

Soon you will draw a map of the objects in your kitten room. A map looks down on a room from above—like you are a giant looking down at tiny shapes!

A table and a book both look like rectangles from above.

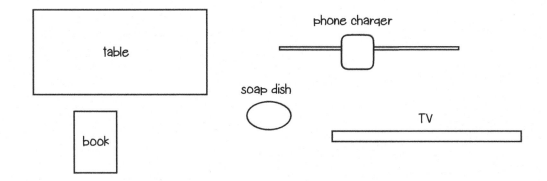

Draw some map shapes of your own. What do these things look like from above?

| litter box | chair | plant | trash basket |
| scratch post | playpen | cabinet | cat bed |

DAY 24: MEASURING KITTEN FURNITURE

On Day 24, you made a list of the objects you want in your kitten room. Today you will **measure the length and width** of each item.

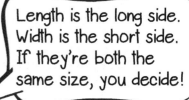

Length is the long side. Width is the short side. If they're both the same size, you decide!

KITTEN ROOM SUPPLY LIST	LENGTH	WIDTH

✳ **STEP 1:** Get a ruler or tape measure.

✳ **STEP 2:** Choose an object from your list.

✳ **STEP 3:** Measure the length and width (if you have the object), or make a close guess about its size (if you don't).

✳ **STEP 4:** Write the measurements in the chart above. Write "in" for inches or "ft" for feet next to each measurement.

2 feet

2 feet

✳ **STEP 5:** Repeat with all the items on your list.

DAY 25: DRAWING KITTEN FURNITURE

Your kitten room map will be made of **shapes that show the actual size** of objects. Here is a section of a kitten room map to show what this looks like.

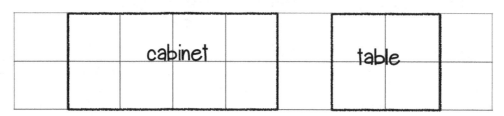

Your kitten room map is made of squares that are 1 foot long and 1 foot wide.

✳ **The cabinet in the map above is 4 feet long and 2 feet wide. How can you know this just by looking at the map?**

    ☐ you can guess it because it's bigger than a table

    ☐ you can tell by counting the squares across and down

    ☐ there's no way to know that unless it's written down

✳ **What size is the table?** _____ feet long and _____ feet wide

Now you try! The squares on the grid below are 1 foot long and 1 foot wide.

✳ **Draw a cat hammock (rectangle) that is 3 feet long and 2 feet wide.**

✳ **Draw a round scratching post that is 2 feet long and 2 feet wide.**

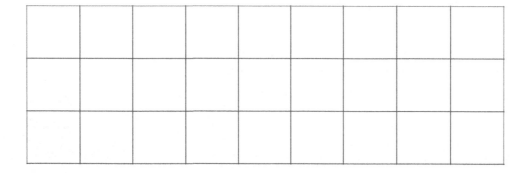

ROUNDING MAKES MATH EASIER

When a play mat is 2 feet long and 2 feet wide, it's pretty easy to draw on a map with 1-foot squares. **But how do you draw it if it's 23 inches long and 21 inches wide?**

Rounding means changing to an easy number that is very close to the original number.

$.99 → $1.00

For example, "one dollar" is easier to work with than 99 cents, and "one foot" is easier than 13 inches.

Here is a number line that shows feet and inches.

INCHES
0 1 2 3 4 5 6 7 8 9 10 11 12 13 14 15 16 17 18 19 20 21 22 23 24 25 26 27 28 29 30 31 32 33 34 35 36 37 38 39 40 41 42 43 44 45 46 47 48

FEET   I foot   2 feet   3 feet   4 feet

1. **What do you notice about how this number line works?**

   _____

2. Some numbers match up exactly. **Two feet is equal to _____ inches.**
   And 48 inches is equal to _____ feet.

3. Other numbers don't match up exactly. We can **round numbers** to make it easier.
   Example: **23 inches is close to _____ feet**, so we can draw 23 inches as 2 feet on our map. **How would you round 14 inches? _____ feet**

   45 inches rounds to _____ feet   6 inches rounds to _____ feet

   19 inches rounds to _____ feet   27 inches rounds to _____ feet

   38 inches rounds to _____ feet   43 inches rounds to _____ feet

QUESTIONS FROM CLEVER KIDS

> I is confused. Has questions!

* _**"I thought you always round up when a number ends in 5?"**_

In rounding, we change to the closest easy number. "Easy numbers" are often tens: 10, 20, 30, 40, etc. There are 9 stops between 1 and 10. **The middle number is 5.** So in this case, our rule is that when it ends in 5, (right in the middle), round up.

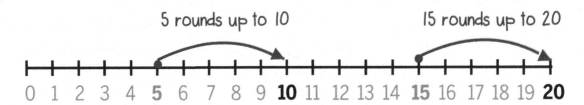

When we round from inches to feet, feet are the "easy numbers". There are 12 inches in one foot, which means there are 11 stops between 1 and 12. **The middle number is 6.** So in this case, when you land on a number that ends in 6 you round up.

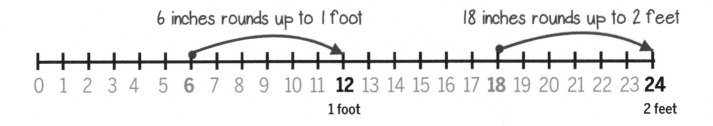

* _**"If I measure 18 inches, can I say it's 1 ½ feet instead of rounding up to 2 feet?"**_

Absolutely! If you did this, you would draw your shape to fill one and a half squares.

Rounding can make things like designing a kitten room easier. But you can always choose to be more precise if you need to be.

* _**"I've seen area measurements written lots of different ways. Which one is the right way?"**_

ALL of these are correct ways. Pick the one you like best!

> 4 feet by 2 feet

> 4 x 2 square feet

> 4 feet long and 2 feet wide

> 4 x 2 ft²

> 4 x 2 sq. ft.

DAY 26: DESIGNING YOUR KITTEN ROOM

Time for the fun part...creating your kitten room! 😃

1. Go back to your list and measurements on Day 25.

KITTEN ROOM SUPPLY LIST	LENGTH	WIDTH
scratching post	2 ft	2 ft

2. **Round your measurements** to feet to make the numbers easier to work with. Write the new measurements in your chart on Day 25.

3. **Take a picture of the chart on Day 25** with your phone so you don't need to hold this book open or flip pages back and forth.

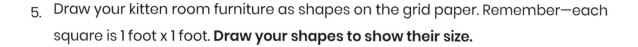

4. Go to artfulmath.com/kitten-goodies to **print several of the grid pages** (the one with squares), or tear out those pages in the back of this book.

5. Draw your kitten room furniture as shapes on the grid paper. Remember—each square is 1 foot x 1 foot. **Draw your shapes to show their size.**

6. **Label each shape** with its name and measurements.

7. **Color and cut out** each shape.

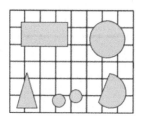

8. Move the shapes around the empty kitten room map on the next page, until **you find the arrangement you like best.**

Your kitten room is 9 feet x 10 feet. Glue your shapes to your kitten room map below. Add decorations to show your unique style!

DOOR

DAY 27: PLAY "CROWDED RECTANGLES" GAME

Watch the video of this game at **artfulmath.com/kitten-goodies**

PLAYERS: 2-3 players

YOU NEED: grid paper (the kind with squares), markers, two dice

1. Get one piece of grid paper to use as your game board. Give each player a different-colored marker.

2. **Roll the dice.**  I rolled a 6 and 2.

3. Draw a rectangle on the board in your color with those dimensions.

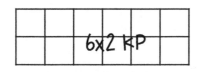

6x2 KP

I can make a rectangle that is 6 squares x 2 squares.

4. Write the dimensions and your initials inside the rectangle.

5. Take turns drawing rectangles in your color to fill up the board.

6. The winner is the last person who is able to make a rectangle.

🌪 LEVEL UP

*   For a more challenging game, make a rule that each of your rectangles must touch another rectangle of your color at a side or corner.

64

FOREVER HOME

Helping Kittens In Need

Real-World Kitten Math

Making a Kitten Blanket

Foster Kitten Story Puzzle

DAY 28: HELPING KITTENS IN NEED

You have learned so much about caring for baby kittens. Fostering is just one of the ways you can help kittens in your community.

Check the boxes to show how you would like to help kittens near you...

GET CRAFTY

▨ make a kitten toy   ▨ sew a snuggle buddy   ▨ make a kitten blanket

VOLUNTEER

▨ foster kittens   ▨ volunteer at a shelter   ▨ snuggle & socialize kittens

MORE THINGS YOU CAN DO

▨ raise money for a shelter   ▨ make adoption posters   ▨ tell friends about fostering

REAL-WORLD KITTEN MATH

Your mom gives you $24 for materials so you can make kitten toys for your foster kittens. Each toy costs you $3.00 to make. **How many toys can you make?** _____

A snuggle buddy is a stuffed animal that makes baby kittens feel safe and warm. You make two snuggle buddies each day for 15 days. **How many snuggle buddies can you donate to the shelter?** _____

You make a kitten blanket that is 36 inches long and 24 inches wide. **What size is your blanket in feet?** _____ feet long and _____ feet wide.
In area measurement, this is _____ square feet.

A one-week-old kitten has a tiny belly and eats every 2 hours. **How many times a day (including night time) would you need to feed a one-week-old kitten?**
_____ times a day

You and your two best friends decide to volunteer at the animal shelter together over the summer. You all worked the same number of hours—a total of 33 hours altogether. **How many hours did each of you work?** _____ hours

Last week you went to the kitten rescue to pet and snuggle with baby kittens. You snuggled with 4 kittens on Tuesday, 6 kittens on Wednesday, 5 on Friday and 8 on Saturday. **How many kittens did you snuggle with during the week?** _____ kittens

The kitten rescue Itty Bitty Orphan Kitty needs $250 to help a sick kitten. You sell lemonade to raise funds. After spending $35 on supplies, you earn $44 on Friday, $170 on Saturday, and $172 on Sunday. **Did you make enough money to meet your goal?** _____

You make posters to get people to visit a kitten fair and adopt kittens. You figure out that for every poster you make, about 10 people visit the fair. You made 5 posters. **About how many people visited the fair?** _____

After you told your friends about fostering kittens, three of them started fostering kittens too. Then each of them had three friends who became fosters. **How many kids were fostering kittens, including you?** _____ kids

What would be your favorite way to help kittens? _____

Why? _____

_____

DAY 29: MAKING A KITTEN BLANKET

Kittens in shelters feel scared and miss their mom. A soft blanket of their own gives them a soft, snuggly place to cuddle until they get a foster home or are adopted.

Follow this pattern to make an easy, no-sew blanket that you can donate to your local animal shelter.

You will need:
- 1/2 yard of fleece fabric in a cute pattern
- 1/2 yard of fleece fabric in a solid color
- Sharp scissors
- Cardboard scraps
- Measuring tape or ruler
- Washable marker

width: _____ inches

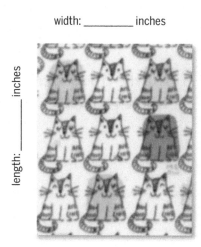

1. **Put one piece of fleece on top of the other, with the good sides facing out.**

2. **Make sure they are exactly the same size.** If not, trim the ends so they are the same size.

3. **What size is your piece of fleece fabric?** (length and width)

   _____ inches x _____ inches

4. **Line up the edges** so they are even.

5. **Measure and cut out a 4x4 inch square of cardboard.**

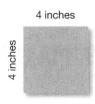

4 inches

4 inches

6. Put your cardboard square on a corner. **Trace and cut to make a notch in the corner**, like in the picture. Repeat with the other three corners.

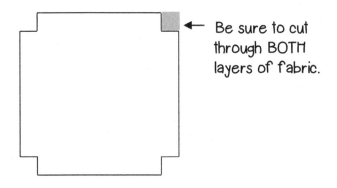

← Be sure to cut through BOTH layers of fabric.

7. **Cut another piece of cardboard that is 4 inches long and 1 inch wide.**

1 inch

4 inches

8. Use the small cardboard piece to help you **draw lines where you will cut your fringe.**

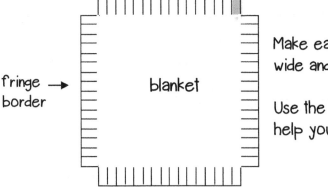

fringe → border

blanket

Make each fringe one inch wide and 4 inches long.

Use the cardboard strip to help you draw the lines.

9. **Cut along the lines** to make the fringe. Cut through both layers of fabric at the same time.

10. Find two pieces of fringe that are next to each other. **Tie the two pieces together. Then tie them together once more to make a double knot.**

11. **Repeat**, tying together all the loose pieces of fringe.

12. Congratulations... you have a gorgeous, finished kitten blanket!

13. Wash your blanket. Then find an animal shelter near you and ask how you can donate your blanket. 🐱🎉🐱

Ha ha, puppies on a kitten blanket.
The kittens get to show those puppies who's boss!

DAY 30: FOSTER KITTEN STORY PUZZLE

Here is a letter from one of your foster kittens.

Fill in the blanks with numbers to finish your kitten's story.

Hello—-meow! I am a kitten and I would like to tell you my story.

I was just _____ weeks old when a kind person found me and brought me and my siblings to our new mom.

Mom doesn't look like us. Our "mom" has just two legs and no fur—except a little bit of fur on top of the head. It's kind of funny.

All I remember from those early days is drinking from a bottle, peeing into a tissue, and drooling into my blanket. Mom says I slept _____ hours per day! It's hard to believe, but I guess babies sleep a lot.

Mom gave us _____ kisses and _____ cuddles every single day. I mostly liked it, but sometimes I got wiggly.

I love to play. Mom calls me Bouncy Pouncy cause I jump around so much. Once I did _____ jumps in one hour! Pretty sure that's a world record.

Our kitten room was awesome, like the best playground ever. If I had to guess how many toys we had, I bet we had _____ toys, and we played with every single one. My kitten friends were all jealous!

Now that I'm big, I'm ready to go to my forever home! I'm a teeny bit scared but mostly excited. My best buddy sibling is going with me. We both hope our new family has a _____-year-old kid for us to play with.

My foster mom was the best ever! My siblings and I think our mom should foster _____ more orphan kittens in the future so they can have as great a life as we do. Thanks kitty momma, we love you!

TURN YOUR STORY INTO A PUZZLE

Now for the fun part…turning your kitten's story into a tricky puzzle for a friend to solve!

1. **Look back at your kitten's story, with all the numbers now filled in.**

    Find the first underlined number in the story. In this example, the first number is 3.

> I was just _____3_____ weeks old when a kind person found me and brought me and my siblings to our new mom.

2. **Make up a math problem that has that number (3) as the answer.**

You may want to try out a few different math problems on scratch paper,

then choose the trickiest one for your puzzle.

$$7-4 \qquad 6\div 2 \qquad 1+1+1 \qquad 2\times 5-7 \qquad (4+2)\div(20-18)$$

4. **On the next page, you'll see a story just like the one you just filled in. This time,**

write your math problem in that space.

> I was just ___(4+2)÷(20-18)___ weeks old when a kind person found me and brought me and my siblings to our new mom.

5. **Repeat until all the spaces in your story puzzle are filled in with math problems.**

6. **Give your kitten math puzzle to a friend to solve!**

FOSTER KITTEN STORY PUZZLE, PART 2

Write a math problem in each space below. See the previous page for how to do this. **Give your story puzzle to a friend to solve.**

Hello—-meow! I am a kitten and I would like to tell you my story.

I was just _____ weeks old when a kind person found me and brought me and my siblings to our new mom.

Mom doesn't look like us. Our "mom" has just two legs and no fur—except a little bit of fur on top of the head. It's kind of funny.

All I remember from those early days is drinking from a bottle, peeing into a tissue, and drooling into my blanket. Mom says I slept _____ hours per day! It's hard to believe, but I guess babies sleep a lot.

Mom gave us _____ kisses and _____ cuddles every single day. I mostly liked it, but sometimes I got wiggly.

I love to play. Mom calls me Bouncy Pouncy cause I jump around so much. Once I did _____ jumps in one hour! Pretty sure that's a world record.

Our kitten room was awesome, like the best playground ever. If I had to guess how many toys we had, I bet we had _____ toys, and we played with every single one. My kitten friends were all jealous!

Now that I'm big, I'm ready to go to my forever home! I'm a teeny bit scared but mostly excited. My best buddy sibling is going with me. We both hope our new family has a _____-year-old kid for us to play with.

My foster mom was the best ever! My siblings and I think our mom should foster _____ more orphan kittens in the future so they can have as great a life as we do. Thanks kitty momma, we love you!

DAY 31: PLAY "WORLD'S BEST BINGO" GAME

*Print the "World's Best Bingo" game board and watch the video
of how to play this game at **artfulmath.com/kitten-goodies**.*

PLAYERS: 1 or more players

YOU NEED: one die, World's Best Bingo game board

1. **Roll the die 4 times.** Write these four numbers at the top of your game board

2. **Use ALL FOUR of the numbers you rolled to create a math problem:**
    - You must use **ALL the numbers exactly once**
      (*unless you rolled the same number twice, then use that number twice*)
    - **Do not use any other numbers** in your math problem
    - Use the **same four numbers** for the entire game
    - You may use **any kind of math** except decimals or rounding
    - **You may combine digits** to make a larger number.

    > EXAMPLE: You rolled a 2, 4, 5 and 1.
    >
    > Make any math problem that uses all four numbers, such as:
    >
    > $2 \times 5 - 4 - 1 = 5$ $\qquad$ $42 + 5 + 1 = 22$ $\qquad$ $24 - 15 = 9$ $\qquad$ $(5+4) - (2+1) = 6$
    >
    > **Then you would cross off the numbers 5, 22, 9 and 6 from your bingo board!**

3. **Tell the other players** when you have a solution and say how you got that
    number. Then **cross that number off the board.**

4. **Cross off 5 in a row to get "Bingo"**... or cross off ALL the squares for "Blackout"!

MEET KELLI'S KITTENS...

Hope

Flossie

Hi, I'm Kelli, the author of Kitten Math

I am a math teacher and kitten foster in real life. I'm the creator of Artful Math—a way of learning math with pictures, patterns, puzzles, and play.

Jimmy

Meet Hope, Flossie, Millie, Sammy, Mochi, Jimmy, & Pip

The kittens on this page were all rescues. I fostered them when they were tiny wee fluff balls that could curl up in the palm of your hand.

Each one of these adorable kittens have their pictures somewhere inside the pages of Kitten Math. **Can you find them all?**

Millie

What comes next?

STEP 1: Leave a **review on Amazon** to share what you thought of Kitten Math.
STEP 2: Fill out your **certificate** on the next page—you earned it!
STEP 3: Find your **next fun math project** at <u>artfulmath.com</u>

See you again soon!

Sammy

Sammy

Mochi

Millie

Jimmy

Pip

KITTEN MATH

ACHIEVEMENT AWARD

IS PRESENTED TO: _____

ON THIS DATE OF: _____

ANSWER KEY

Day 1 PICKING OUT YOUR KITTENS: Look at a calendar and find today's date. Count back 3 weeks or 21 days to find their birthday. Count forward 5 weeks or 35 days to find their adoption day.

THE KITTEN QUESTIONS GAME: Answers will vary. Check your answers on a calculator.

Day 2 KITTEN NAME MATH CODE: Answers will vary—there are lots of creative names that come close to $100! Here are some names that add up to $100 exactly:

Buzzy, Drizzle, Pistachio, Grumpy, Flurry, Splashy, Tallahatchie, Wriggles, Marjory, Starling, Wednesday and Squint

(At least, I THINK they add up to $100. You could always check and let me know if I got one wrong. 😊)

Day 4 WHAT DO BABY KITTENS NEED?
- Weigh kittens (100+200+50) = scale = 350 grams
- Soft blankets (34-11) = blanket = 23 hours
- Heating pad (2x40) = Snugglesafe = 80 degrees
- Tissues (20+60+4) = Kleenex = 84 tissues per day
- KMR formula (20÷2) = KMR can = 10 days

POOPY PUZZLES
- You washed 28 swaddle blankets
- 7 loads of laundry
- 4 loads of laundry
- 24 tissues, 12 wet wipes, and 1 towel
- 96 tissues, 48 wet wipes, and 4 towels

Day 5 DO YOU HAVE ENOUGH MONEY?
$15, $10, $25, $9, $13, $7, $6, $8

A price ending in .99 feels a lot cheaper than something that costs one penny more. $14.99 sounds like a much lower price than $15, even when you know it's just 1 cent less.

Day 7 THINK OF DECIMALS LIKE MONEY

- 5.24 = 5 dollars, 2 dimes, 4 pennies
- 9.4 = 9 dollars, 4 dimes, 0 pennies
- 9.40 = 9 dollars, 4 dimes, 0 pennies
- 9.4 and 9.40 are the same amount. Adding a zero to a decimal doesn't change it. It's like adding "zero pennies" to 9 dollars and 4 dimes.
- She is correct. 13.5 and 13.50 are the same amount.
- 15.3 (or 15.30) is greater than 15.18. 12.33 is larger than 12.29
- 12.33 is is greater than 12.29
- .7 is greater than .56
- 3.45 is greater than .34
- .31 is greater than .13
- 17.0 is larger than 7.10
- 120.9 is larger than 120.39

- The second number line is part of the first one. When you zoom in on the first number line between 0.5 and 0.6, there are smaller decimal numbers. These are shown on the second number line. The second number line shows numbers that are ten times smaller than the first one.
- .311 is larger than .133
- 1.39 is larger than 1.298
- .345 is larger than .34
- Sasquatch gained more weight (0.9 is greater than 0.57).
- Sasquatch gained MORE than half an ounce (half an ounce = .5 ounce)
- Fluffpug gained LESS than one ounce.
- Answers may vary (ex: .55, .7, .39, .99, etc)
- Answers may vary (ex: .91, .93, .98 etc)

Day 9 HOW OFTEN SHOULD KITTENS EAT?

- *How often should you feed 3-week-old kittens?* every 4 hours
- *How much should a 3-week-old kitten eat per feeding?* 14 ml
- *How many times per day should you feed a 3-week-old kitten?* 6 times per day
- *How much should a 3-week-old kitten eat per day?* 14 ml x 6 = 84 ml per day
- *What does 'ml' mean?* milliliters
- *What pattern is in the "weight" column?* Kittens gain 100 grams per week
- *What pattern is in the "amount per feeding" column?* + 4 per week
- *Why do kittens eat fewer times per day as they grow?* Their bellies grow bigger and they can eat more food at each feeding, so they don't need to eat as often.

Day 10 MAKE A FEEDING SCHEDULE:

1-4: Answers will vary

Feeding schedules: Answers will vary

A 3-week-old kitten needs to eat 6 times per day.

5-week-old kittens eat about 4 times per day.

Day 11 KITTEN FEEDING PUZZLERS

Widget will need to eat again at 7:00pm and 9:00pm.

Fluffernutter will need to eat again at 3:00pm and 6:00pm.

Maise needs to eat again at 1:00pm and 5:00pm.

Jellybean needs to eat again at 8:00pm and 1:00am.

SPENDING TIME WITH KITTENS

- **60** minutes
- Favorite kitten activities may vary
- 30 minutes each
- Kitten activities may vary
- 15 minutes each
- You peek at your kittens 12 times in one hour
- You play with your kittens 3 times per day
- 30 minutes

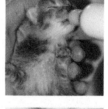

Day 13 HOW TO BOTTLE FEED A KITTEN: These two pictures show the **wrong** way to feed a kitten (on its back). All the other pictures show the correct way to feed a kitten.

MIXING KITTEN FORMULA: 1 scoop powder with 2 scoops water; 4 scoops powder with 8 scoops water; 6 scoops powder with 12 scoops water

KITTEN RATIO PUZZLERS

- 8 spoonfuls
- 12 spoonfuls
- 12 spoonfuls
- 15 spoonfuls

Day 14: ARE YOUR KITTENS EATING ENOUGH?

There are 4 measurement lines on the bottle.

If you fill to the top line, there are 60ml of formula in a bottle.

Each line measures 15 ml.

If you start with a full bottle to the top line, and the first kitten eats 12 ml, 48 ml are left.

14 x 4 = 56. A bottle holds 60ml. One bottle will feed four 3-week-old kittens.

It's a little hard to see the numbers in the photos. The lines, from bottom to top, are 15ml, 30ml, 45ml, and 60ml.

Kitten 1 ate about 20ml.

Kitten 2 ate about 12ml.

Kitten 3 ate about 14ml.

Kitten 4 ate about 15ml.

Kitten 2 ate a little less than the average at this feeding. You should keep an eye on this kitten and make sure she's getting enough at other feedings and gaining weight.

Day 16 WEIGHING YOUR KITTENS

The kitten who gained the most weight is the one ending with the weight 439.

97 grams

54 grams

31 grams

13 grams

Which kitten's data is shown? The first kitten in the chart

What do the numbers along the side mean? weight in grams

What do the numbers at the bottom mean? dates

What do the round dots show? how much the kitten weighs each day

What do you predict the kitten's weight might be on 4-8? Answers may vary.

BECOMING A KITTEN DETECTIVE

- ***Did this kitten lose weight?*** Answers may vary.
- ***What did the weights reveal?*** Answers may vary.
- ***What would a line graph of a sick kitten NOT look like?***
- ***How can you tell when a kitten starts feeling better?*** 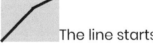 The line starts going up.

Day 18 WHAT DO GROWING KITTENS NEED?

- cuddle and wrestle — stuffed animal toys
- eat from a dish — kitten food and dishes
- go potty in a litter box — litter box
- scratch, sharpen claws — scratching post
- jump — flying bird toys
- chase things — balls, toy mice

HALF OFF ALL KITTEN TOYS

50% off $6.00 is $3.00
50% off $12.04 is $6.02
50% off $24.00 is $12.00
50% off $30.18 is $15.09
50% off $8.00 is $4.00
50% off $28.60 is $14.30
50% off $14.20 is $7.10
50% off $10.12 is $5.06
50% off $42.88 is $21.44
50% off $16.30 is $8.15

Day 19 HALF OFF TRICKY NUMBERS

50% off $9.99 is $5.00
50% off $11.99 is $6.00
50% off $5.99 is $3.00
50% off $15.99 is $8.00
50% off $4.27 is $2.14
50% off $8.15 is $4.08
50% off $16.49 is $8.25
50% off $26.13 is $13.07
50% off $12.99 is $6.50
50% off $23.99 is $12.00
50% off $6.99 is $3.50
50% off $22.99 is $11.50

Day 22 WHAT IS AREA?

- area
- Area is the amount of **space** inside a **shape**.
- The area of this rectangle is 16 square feet
- 8 feet x 2 feet = 16 square feet
- The area of this rectangle is 32 square feet
- 8 feet x 4 feet = 32 square feet
- I counted 90 squares. That's 90 square feet.
- 10 x 9 = 90 The area is 90 square feet.

KITTEN ROOM AREA PUZZLES

- 24 square feet
- 48 square feet
- 55 square feet
- 24 square feet

Day 23 WHAT GOES IN THE KITTEN ROOM?

Kitten Room Supply List: Answers will vary, but may include: litter box, sofa, chair, table or cabinet, cat bed(s), trash can, kitten playpen, play mat, scratching post, large toys.

Possible shapes of furniture might look like:

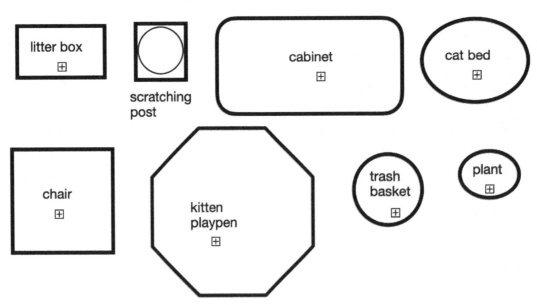

Day 24 MEASURING KITTEN FURNITURE
Objects and measurements may vary.

Day 25 DRAWING KITTEN FURNITURE

- You can tell by counting the squares across and down.
- The table is 2 feet long and 2 feet wide.
- Your cat hammock and scratching post should take up the same number of squares as the picture below. Here are two correct ways you might have drawn your cat hammock:

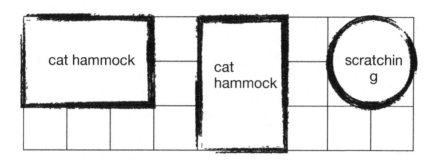

ROUNDING MAKES MATH EASIER

1. Inches match to feet at every 12 inches.
2. Two feet is equal to 24 inches. And 48 inches is equal to 4 feet.
3. 23 inches is close to 2 feet. 14 inches rounds to 1 foot.

- 45 inches rounds to 4 feet
- 19 inches rounds to 2 feet
- 38 inches rounds to 3 feet
- 6 inches rounds to 1 foot
- 27 inches rounds to 2 feet
- 43 inches rounds to 4 feet

Day 28: REAL WORLD KITTEN MATH

- *How many toys did you make?* 8 toys
- *How many snuggle buddies can you donate?* 30 snuggle buddies
- *What size is your blanket in feet?* 3 feet long and 2 feet wide. Area: 6 square feet
- *How many times a day would you feed a 1-week-old kitten?* 12 times per day
- *How many hours did each of you work?* 16 ½ hours each
- *How many kittens did you snuggle with during the week?* 23 kittens
- *Did you make enough money to meet your goal?* yes
- *About how many people visited the fair?* 50 people
- *How many kids were fostering kittens, including you?* 13 kids (1+3+9=13)

Day 30: FOSTER KITTEN LETTER

- Answers and math problems will vary

GAME BOARDS

On the following pages, you will find
game boards for all the games in Kitten Math.
They can be copied from the book or printed online.

To print the game boards out on your printer,
sign in to access the online bonuses page at
artfulmath.com/kitten-goodies

- Cross Out Singles
- Round Four
- Speedy School Day
- Euclid's Game
- Snugglenumber
- Crowded Rectangles
- World's Best Bingo Game
- Kitten Room Grid

CROSS OUT SINGLES

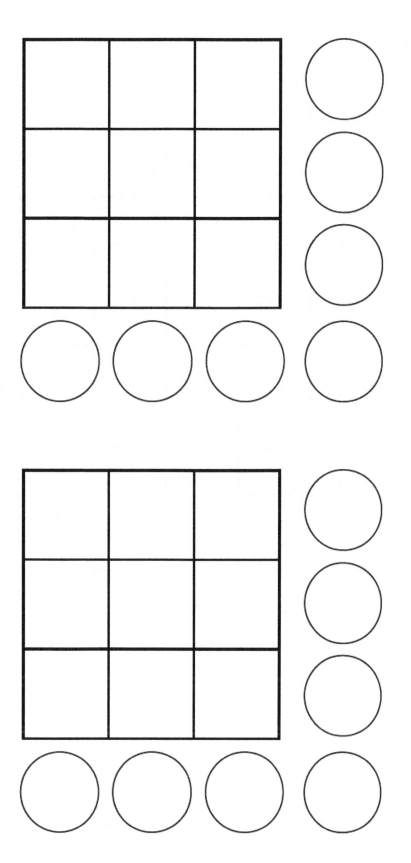

ROUND FOUR

1	2	3	4	5	6	7
11	12	13	14	15	16	17
21	22	23	24	25	26	27
31	32	33	34	35	36	37
41	42	43	44	45	46	47
51	52	53	54	55	56	57
61	62	63	64	65	66	67
71	72	73	74	75	76	77

SPEEDY SCHOOL DAY

PLAYER 1

DIE ROLL	TIMES 10	TIME
_ _ _ _ _ _ _	_ _ _ _ _ _	9:00

PLAYER 2

DIE ROLL	TIMES 10	TIME
_ _ _ _ _ _	_ _ _ _ _ _	9:00

EUCLID'S GAME

1	2	3	4	5	6	7	8	9	10
11	12	13	14	15	16	17	18	19	20
21	22	23	24	25	26	27	28	29	30
31	32	33	34	35	36	37	38	39	40
41	42	43	44	45	46	47	48	49	50
51	52	53	54	55	56	57	58	59	60
61	62	63	64	65	66	67	68	69	70
71	72	73	74	75	76	77	78	79	80
81	82	83	84	85	86	87	88	89	90
91	92	93	94	95	96	97	98	99	100

SNUGGLENUMBER

GAME 1

0 ____

5 ____

10 ____ ____

25 ____ ____

50 ____ ____

100 ____ ____

GAME 2

0 ____

5 ____

10 ____ ____

25 ____ ____

50 ____ ____

100 ____ ____

CROWDED RECTANGLES

WORLD'S BEST BINGO GAME

_____ _____ _____ _____

KITTEN ROOM GRID

Each square = 1 foot x 1 foot.

Made in the USA
Columbia, SC
05 December 2021

50458792R10057